THE BIRDS
AND THE BEES

THE BIRDS AND THE BEES

BY
JOHN D. JESS

A compilation of radio messages
on little-known facts of nature revealing
the marvel of God's handiwork

MOODY PRESS
CHICAGO

Moody Paperback Edition, 1976

By permission of
The Chapel of the Air, Inc.

Second Printing, 1978

ISBN: 0-8024-0549-5

Printed in the United States of America.

Contents

Preface

To convey in word the wonders of God's creation in a way simple enough to arrest the attention of both young and old, and brief enough to keep auditor and/or reader interest at a high level is not easy—at least for me. There is so much material on the subjects dealt with in the following pages that the greatest problem has been in sorting and abridging it.

The science-oriented reader may chafe at the cursory and nontechnical manner in which the subjects have been treated. But it should be borne in mind that this was necessary in order to pare the subject matter to accommodate about twelve minutes of air time and to gear it, for the most part, to those untrained in the terminology of science.

Each of the following addresses was given over a large network of radio stations in the United States and overseas. So enthusiastic was listener response that The Chapel staff felt the material should be preserved in printed form. This has since proved to be a rewarding decision.

With these facts in mind, I trust you will regard indulgently the brevity and simplicity of these radio addresses and gain a new awareness of our God's majesty and grace!

1
The Birds

Their mechanical equipment—
wings, propellers, steering gear—
approximates the airplane.

Not long ago I heard a broadcast on which a number of university students were interviewed with respect to their religious beliefs. Only one, as I recall, said he believed in God. All the others claimed to be either agnostics or atheists.

One particular student, when asked what he considered the strongest argument in favor of atheism, replied, "There is no evidence of God anywhere."

I was reminded of the legal battle between Rufus Choate and Daniel Webster over a century ago. The case involved a decision as to whether two wagon wheels belonged to the same axle. Choate presented a brilliant argument on the theory of the "fixation of points" by which he contended that the wheels came from the same axle. About the time he had the jury convinced, Daniel Webster requested that the wheels and axle be produced for the jury to *examine*. It was immediately evident that they could not have come from the same axle because they were not the right size.

Addressing the jury, Webster said, "Gentlemen, all you need do is look at those wheels. Your eyes will tell you they could not have come from the same axle."

The jury agreed, and Webster won the case.

I am always stunned when I hear someone say there is no evidence for God in the universe, for one does not need a brilliant argument for God; he needs only eyes and a logical mind. As Webster summed up the axle and wheel case by merely asking the jury to look, so the psalmist summed up his case for a Creator when he said, "The heavens declare the glory of God; and the firmament sheweth his handywork" (Ps 19:1).

Only I don't think we need the heavens to prove God. Perhaps we need only the birds and the bees.

Although this combination of nouns has come to convey the idea of sex education, we shall look at them as evidences of divine creation. If you cannot see God in our planetary system, perhaps you will discern Him when you consider the birds and bees (although a study of any of the million other forms of life would be just as intriguing and convincing).

Birds, to me, are a forceful witness to a divine origin. According to the *Encyclopaedia Brittanica*, there are between 10,000 and 12,000 known species of birds. We must limit ourselves in this study to only a few of the physical and instinctual aspects of some birds—their bills, wings, nests, and navigational aptitudes.

Evolutionists insist that birds evolved from reptiles, but who can honestly conceive of scales turning to feathers? And how can solid bones become hollow to make flight not only convenient but possible?

A bird's bones are filled with a spongy network which fills with air as it breathes! Imagine air cavities in bones connected to the bird's lungs! Yet, no strength is sacrificed, for the light, hollow bones are stiffened with ridges that resemble advanced engineering techniques. It has been said that the braces within the bone of a vulture's wings are almost identical, geometrically speaking, with those of the Warren truss commonly used in steel structure.

A bird is actually a living airplane. John H. Storer, writing in the *Scientific American,* says a bird flies by the same aerodynamic principle as a plane. He says, "It uses much of the same mechanical equipment—wings, propellers, steering gear, even slots and flaps for help in taking off and landing."

You may be interested, as I was, in his use of the word "propeller":

11

> Astonishing as it may seem, every bird has a pair of "propellers".... They can be seen in action best in a slow motion picture of a bird in flight. During the downward beat of the wings the primary feathers at the wing tips stand out at right angles to the rest of the wing and to the line of flight.
>
> These feathers are the propellers. They take on this twisted form for only a split second during each wing beat.... Throughout the entire wing beat they are constantly changing their shape, adjusting automatically to air pressure and the changing requirement of the wing as it moves up and down.

Notice particularly Dr. Storer's use of the term "adjusting automatically." Name just one thing that adjusts automatically that was not designed. Modern technology has given us hundreds of automatic contrivances—furnaces, air conditioners, toasters, engine chokes, light switches, and lawn sprinklers—to name but a fraction of the total—but not one is the product of happenstance. They were skillfully and laboriously designed and perfected by intelligent scientists and engineers.

Now if a bird's wing does something "automatically," it had to be designed. Nothing automatic just happens.

Any ornithologist will tell you a bird's wing is elaborately and ingeniously fashioned. It is self-adjusting, as though controlled by an electronic switch or computer that reacts in a thousandth part of a second!

Birds, incidentally, are the fastest creatures on our planet. The peregrine falcon, for example, can dive on its prey at speeds up to 180 miles an hour, yet it remains under perfect control. The African eagle swoops down at speeds averaging one hundred miles an hour, then comes to a complete stop by spreading its wings and tail in an aerial skid stop within a space of twenty feet!

Consider a bird's keen eyesight. When a bird of prey swoops down on its quarry, its eyes are kept in perfect focus as the distance rapidly narrows. A third eyelid, which is drawn back and forth across the eyeball like a windshield wiper, keeps the eyeball free of dust and other irritants. No one has ever suggested, to my knowledge, that such devices on automobile windshields are the result of a fortuitous evolutionary process.

No less ingenious is a bird's beak which accommodates perfectly to its food needs. Birds that live on tough-shelled nuts have heavy beaks, capable of crushing rigid shells. Hawks, owls, and eagles have hooked beaks which permit them to tear apart their prey. Scavengers like vultures also have hooked bills, but these are softer because the flesh of dead animals tears off more easily than that of live ones. Birds depending on grubs and insects that live in the bark of trees have long, straight beaks designed for boring. Geese and ducks have spoon bills suitable for foraging food from the bottom of lakes and ponds.

To whom shall we credit this amazing versatility? An impersonal, random something called "Chance"? Or to the birds themselves?

(If, by the way, their bills gradually adapted to their needs through a long evolutionary process, how did birds survive while this process was taking place?)

Not the least of a bird's amazing skills is its nest-building abilities. Here again the touch of genius demands a Designer, One who built into these feathered creatures the ability to build their own homes in a manner that would baffle most men.

The tailorbird, for example, sews large leaves together with fibers when building its nest, using its beak for a needle! The chimney swift builds nests of twigs by "pasting" them to the inside of a hollow tree or an unused chimney. The glue is manufactured in its mouth! Why would only a chimney swift have a glue factory in its mouth? Why not other birds?

The Baltimore oriole builds the most complicated nest of all. By means of thousands of shuttlelike movements of its bill, it makes stitches, knots, and loops. Its nest is so well made it may hang on a tree for years without being dislodged by the elements.

The navigational abilities of birds are perhaps the most amazing of all their skills. It is not known for certain how, without baggage, bedding, lunch, compass, or map, they make incredibly long trips they have never made before. A golden plover flies from Canada to South America without stopping! A little bird called the wheatear, no larger than an English sparrow, travels every year from Africa to Greenland—and on a fixed schedule! The tiny blackpoll warbler nests in Canada, then wings its way four thousand miles away to Brazil!

Much of the traveling is done at night and over immense stretches of water and wilderness. Who tells these birds where to go and when?

One wonders about the objectivity of those who say there is no evidence of God in the universe. What about birds?

Jesus said in Matthew 6:26, "Behold the fowls of the air: for they sow not, neither do they reap, nor gather into barns; yet your heavenly Father feedeth them. Are ye not much better than they?"

From my study of birds I deduce that God is very fond of them to have made them so fearfully and wonderfully, and to so tenderly care for them. Is it not thrilling to know that He loves us much more? (Lk 12:6-7)

One of my favorite poems from the pen and heart of Annie Johnson Flint says,

The little birds trust God, for they go singing
   From Northern woods where autumn winds have
      blown.
With joyous faith their trackless pathway winging
   To summer lands of song, afar, unknown.

And if He cares for them through wintry weather,
   And will not disappoint one little bird,
Will He not be as true a heavenly Father
   To every soul who trusts His holy Word?

Let us go singing, then, and not go sighing
   Since we are sure our times are in His hand.
Why should we weep, and fear, and call it dying?—
   'Tis only flitting to a Summer land!

2
The Bees

Their system of wing structure is so
complicated man has never
come close to duplicating its
aerodynamic design.

Thirteen to fifteen years of academic nurture
have failed to convince many students in higher
education that for every design there must be a
designer, and where there is intelligence there
must be a personality. Many, unfortunately, are
only parroting what they have been told in the
classroom.

It is a bewildering mystery how anyone can
study the "lowly" bee and remain unconvinced
that an intelligent Creator had a hand in its
physical makeup and social instincts.

In a colony of 50,000 bees, approximately 60
percent are workers that average some ten trips
a day in the summertime and visit a total of
about 300,000 flowers. They go about this so
arduously that their delicate wings often fray

out in two months' time, resulting in their death.

The study of a bee's instinct and anatomy is so fascinating we do not wonder that naturalists and biologists have written so many books about this hymenopterous insect. When one studies the bee's specialized organs and unique characteristics, complete honesty draws the conclusion that we are dealing not only with a creature but with a Creator as well.

The honeybee has sharp tips on its claws enabling it to walk easily on any rough surface, but it also has little cushions between its claws, called the pulvilli, which enable it to walk on very smooth surfaces, such as glass.

Although the bee's main function is to gather honey, it also performs an essential service, cross-pollination, without which orchards would produce little or no fruit, and many crops could not be grown. It has been estimated that the average yield of insect-impollinated plants totals $5 billion, 80 percent of which may be credited to honeybees. While gathering nectar they pollinate over fifty flowers and agricultural crops. Because of this, one scientist observes, "They are fifty times more valuable to society than the honey they produce."

Each bee has two rodlike projections extending in front which move continuously. These antennae are not only feelers but "smellers." In other words, they are the equivalent of a nose.

Bees have thousands of "sense plates" which, when inserted in nectar-laden flowers, become coated and clogged. This accumulation would soon disorient and destroy the bee were it not for the fact that the Creator has provided it with an ingenious means of cleaning its antennae in order to keep them functioning. How?

On its front legs there is a movable piece of tough tissue which the bee can raise, creating a small opening. On the outer edges of this opening are stiff, short hairs, like a tiny brush. When the antennae need cleaning, the bee simply opens the "gate," draws its antennae back and forth between the stiff hairs, and all dirt and dust are removed!

The wings of a bee are so ingeniously constructed that it is difficult to describe them and their function. Because its body is rather bulky, large wings are required to enable it to fly, yet elongated wings, such as those of the dragonfly, for example, would prevent the bee from entering its narrow six-sided cell in the hive.

Its Designer solved this engineering problem by placing on the rear edge of the larger front wing a ridge that hooks on the back when flying. This converts the four wings into two large wings for flight! When not in flight, the wings are released and overlap, greatly reducing their size and allowing the bee to enter an area much smaller than the larger wings would permit.

In flight, the bee's wings move in a figure-

19

eight design, enabling it to fly in any direction—up, down, side to side, backward or forward—or to hover like a hummingbird. This system of wing structure is so complicated that man has never come close to duplicating it in aerodynamic design.

Bees, like many other insects, have three tiny eyes which provide them with remarkable vision and act as a sort of compass. By merely glancing at any part of the sky during daylight hours, the bee can immediately determine the sun's position, the time of day, and its own position in relation to its hive or a place where there is food.

Bees can also converse. I don't mean they can speak, but they do communicate by means of special movements called "dances," and through scents. The eminent Austrian scientist, Professor Karl von Frisch, demonstrated that the honeybee indicates the presence, position, distance, and direction of pollen and nectar food to other members of the colony by executing little geometric dances. A foraging bee, he says, returning to the hive with a full load of pollen and nectar, will, upon reaching the hive, give all the other bees a sip of nectar from its own mouth. It then begins a little dance, circling to the right, then to the left, repeating it many times. If the bee dances energetically for about thirty seconds, the other bees know there is food nearby.

The other bees then fly out to find the food. They know the kind of flower to look for because of the scent of the nectar on the informant bee. Upon returning to the hive, each bee performs the same dance as the first bee, providing there is plenty of nectar left. If not, the dance is more brief and less vigorous, resulting in fewer bees being stimulated to go to that place.

Bees will fly a mile or more from the hive for their food. However, when this is more than one hundred yards away, they perform a different kind of dance. From the nature of the dance the other bees learn exactly how far away the food is and in what direction! The faster the dance, the closer the food. By a slight tail-wagging motion one bee can tell another the direction in which the food lies. Those that pay attention to this ceremony are able to fly directly to the spot the informer has visited!

Did you know that bees are able to generate heat when they need it? Like all other insects, they are cold-blooded, so the production of heat in a hive calls for a stroke of genius. When the hive is cold, the bees begin a muscular activity which resembles shivering. The colony assembles in a compact cluster, moving rapidly, shaking their bodies, and fanning their wings. By means of this animation they can warm a hive when the outside temperature is below freezing. In the summertime, when the hive is too hot, they gather on the outside and beat their wings vigorously, blowing air into the hive and thus "air conditioning" it!

How did bees learn all this? If, as the evolutionist says, it is the result of millions of years of trial and error, how many errors could a colony of bees survive? If it is the result of a gradually evolving instinct, how did the first bees pull through?

In my judgment there is but one consistent conclusion: the first bees that ever lived knew just as much about cell construction, wax making, the secrets of feeding, communication, and the gathering and making of honey as their present-day descendents. Were it otherwise, they would all have perished before evolution had a chance to get under way!

Therefore, from the very beginning, bees had to know what they know now. Call it instinct or whatever, Someone tells these millions of amazing insects what to do. *And it is not their parents!*

The more we study the amazing creatures that surround us, the more convinced we become that a Designer and Creator places within them the drives and instincts which make them such wonders to behold. It is not astute to charge it all up to some vague force labeled "Nature." Birds and bees, along with all other creatures of God, speak as clearly of an intelligent Designer as an automobile or refrigerator. I would say even more so, for man has never contrived anything that has either instinct or intelligence. Man cannot create even a blade of grass, not to mention a bird or a bee. He can only study them and marvel at the intelligent craftsmanship they represent and how they are divinely motivated to serve man, their supervisor.

While it is fascinating to study the construction and habits of God's many creatures, something much more captivating and important is the impartation of the new nature God gives all who repent of their sins and believe in Jesus Christ, His Son, as their personal Saviour. The "new creation" of 2 Corinthians 5:17 tops them all! Have you experienced it?

3
The Stars

No mathematical equation
within the human mind can be used to
estimate their number.

With the generous assistance of optical and radio telescopes, man has been able to explore the universe in ways that stagger the mind. Einstein's theories notwithstanding, there exists no valid proof that the universe is not infinite. We only know that there is a definite boundary beyond which man cannot hope to probe with his present methods and equipment.

Some astronomers, whose minds are overwhelmed by the concept of infinity, insist the universe must be measurable, that it has a "shell" of some description around it. But if so, what lies outside the shell? More space? Another universe?

However we wish to approach it, space is simply endless—at least as far as the human mind is concerned. "There is no end but an abyss of real immensity," said Immanuel Kant two centuries ago, "in the presence of which all the capability of human conception sinks exhausted."

Does the vastness of the universe tell us anything about ourselves? And God?

I believe it does, for only a God of infinite power could create it, and only a God of infinite love and detail would pick a single grain from the seashore of immeasurable expanse, and people it with intelligent creatures capable of knowing, loving, and serving Him.

Let us therefore apply our minds, insofar as is possible, to the enigma of immensity.

The sun, as every schoolchild knows, is our nearest star. It is a mere 93 million miles from the earth. Compared to Pluto, the farthest-known planet from the sun, the earth is almost within handshaking distance of this giant furnace. (Pluto is about 3 billion 675 million miles away from the sun, compared to earth's 93 million miles.)

Light travels so fast it can circle the earth about seven and one-half times in one second. At this incomprehensible rate of speed, it takes about eight minutes for the sun's light to reach us. By way of comparison, the distance from one side of Pluto's orbit to the other averages about 7 billion, 350 million miles. To speed across the orbit of Pluto, it would take a ray of light something like eleven hours.

But these are puny distances compared to those between other remote star systems.

The nearest sun and planetary system to ours is believed to be Alpha Centauri. Light from this star takes more than four years to reach us.

The distance light travels in a year (called a light-year) is approximately 6 trillion miles!

Peering a little farther into space we see Sirius, the brightest star in our heavens. It is nearly twice as far away as Alpha. Polaris is some 300 light-years away. Our own galaxy, the Milky Way, is about 80,000 light-years in diameter! Since the sun and its little family of planets is some distance from the center of the Milky Way system, some of the suns in our "local" galaxy are 40,000 light-years apart!

What does this tell us about God? David said it in Psalm 103:11: "As the heaven is high above the earth, so great is his mercy toward them that fear him."

You and I should have a much better comprehension of this comparison than David did, for it is doubtful that he had any coherent concept of the true vastness of the heavens concerning which he wrote. The Holy Spirit who moved him to write knew, but David may have thought only in terms of several hundred miles. Today we know much more than he did about the vast distances involved, so our appreciation of God and His handiwork should far exceed David's.

Just as God knew more about what David was saying than David did, so also His knowledge exceeded Isaiah's when He inspired that prophet to write, "For as the heavens are higher than the earth, so are my ways higher than your ways, and my thoughts than your thoughts" (Is 55:9).

Did these men sense the limits of their understanding? I am certain they did. "Such knowledge is too wonderful for me," wrote David in Psalm 139:6, "it is high, I cannot attain unto it." (One can scarcely resist the temptation to compare the humility of David with the egotistical pronouncements of some today who figuratively shake their little fists at God and conduct themselves as though the wonders and vastness of the universe were of their own making.)

A most spectacular astronomical discovery in recent years discloses that no matter in which direction the telescopes are turned, the distant galaxies are all traveling *away from us*. The more remote the galaxy, the more rapid the rate of retreat. Bear in mind that these galaxies are moving away from us at the speed of light— 186,000 miles a second! Where are they going? When, if ever, will they stop?

This is beyond the comprehension of man. We can only parrot the psalmist: "Such knowledge is too wonderful for me ... I cannot attain unto it."

As these great distances are beyond our powers of comprehension, so also are the eternal purposes of God. Those who say they cannot accept the love and greatness of God nevertheless accept the observable facts of the universe. This constitutes a strong indication that men accept only what they want to accept.

Many centuries ago God told Abraham to lift his eyes to the heavens and count the stars, if he could. Then He promised that Abraham's seed would be as numerous as these heavenly bodies. How many stars do you suppose Abraham was able to count?

Astronomers tell us there are not more than 5 or 6,000 stars visible to the naked eye under the most favorable conditions, and only half of these are visible at any one time and place. So at the most, Abraham could have counted no more than 3,000 stars on the night of God's promise. Presumably, even this number overwhelmed him. What if he had possessed a telescope!

In the era of modern telescopes and cameras, we now know that man can only estimate the number of stars in the universe. In the late 1920s astronomers thought there were approximately 300 billion stars. As telescopes improved, that figure has mounted. Recent books on astronomy are hesitant about numbering the stars. One refers to "many thousand million," and it refers only to the stars in our own galaxy!

If there are billions of stars in just one galaxy, how many galaxies are there?

By the spring of 1958 more than 2,700 clusters of galaxies had been cataloged, each cluster containing at least fifty galaxies, with probably as many as 100 billion stars in each!

Incredible? Yes, but bear in mind that these are only the *observed* stars. By means of the radio telescope, developed in recent years, stars which give no visible light can be "heard." Some astronomers, on the basis of this new technique, are telling us that our own galaxy, the Milky Way, contains up to 100 billion such stars. If this is true of our galaxy, it is probably true of others, which means that there is not a mathematical equation within the range of the human mind that can even begin to estimate the number of stars in God's universe.

Sir James Jeans, one of this century's most brilliant astronomers, estimated that the total number of stars in space exceeded the number of grains of sand on all the seashores of the earth! Three or four decades ago that must have sounded like a reckless exaggeration, but it is no longer unbelievable. Indeed it is quite probable that the stars *outnumber* the grains of sand!

If you think the creation of so vast a number of stars a remarkable feat, consider the fact that, according to the inspired psalmist, God has not only numbered the stars, but has *named* them! "He [God] counts the number of the stars; He gives names to all of them" (Ps 147:4, NASB).

No wonder that after receiving the divine inspiration to record this information, the psalmist declares in the following verse: "Great is our Lord, and abundant in strength; His understanding is infinite" (v. 5, NASB).

The honest astronomer will be quick to confess with the psalmist that what he beholds in his lens requires an abundance of power, and "infinite understanding."

One of the most engaging promises in all the Bible is Daniel 12:3: "And they that be wise shall shine as the brightness of the firmament; and they that turn many to righteousness as the stars for ever and ever."

Does this mean that the stars, as well as those who win souls, will shine on forever? The implication is certainly there. God may just keep those great furnaces going throughout all eternity for our continued enjoyment and wonder.

How glad I am to be involved in such an imperishable business!

4
The Eye

*If the lips say one thing and
the eyes another, you had better
believe the eyes!*

The body's imperial organ is the eye. It is
mentioned no less than 534 times in the Bible.

In science's relentless quest for knowledge, it
has done much to remove the mask of mystery
from these twin cameras of the face, yet most
people go to their graves lacking a full appreciation of this creative masterpiece. "If God lacked
anything of infinite wisdom," a famous seer
once said, "He would have failed in creating the
human eye."

Compared to other organs of the body, the eye
unquestionably excels in structure and adapta-
tion. By comparison, the eyes of a bat, a fish, a
mole, or a reptile are simple, the reason being
that they have lesser tasks to perform. Some insects have a score of eyes, but their twenty have
less faculty than two human eyes. A species of

beetle has two eyes above the water and two beneath, yet its four are not equal to our two. When it comes to equipment, man stands supreme!

The late Sir Charles Scott Sherrington, eminent physiologist and one of the most honored scientists of his day, said in a classic essay entitled *The Eye:* "Behind the intricate mechanism of the human eye lie breath-taking glimpses of the Master Plan."

John Perry, in his treatment of the subject, *Our Amazing Eyes,* wrote:

> No scientific instrument is as sensitive to light as your eye. In the dark, its sensitivity increases 10,000 times, and you can detect a faint glow, less than a thousandth as bright as a candle's glow.... You can see light from the stars, the nearest of which apart from the sun, is 24 trillion miles away.

Continuing he says: "The image focused on the lens of the eye falls on the 'screen' at the back of the eyeball, the retina. The retina has about 130 million cells."

Under the title, "Your Remarkable Eyes," *Science Digest* points out the following:

> It is unbelievable with what rapidity the eye works. It has been estimated that from the vast panorama presented by your eyes, each one can send a billion impulses per second to the brain—and then your mind chooses significant details.

You can stare at a sign without becoming aware of its message, while on the other hand a fragmentary glimpse of some familiar object attracts your attention immediately.

The eye's lens is greatly superior to any ground glass lens, and it changes its curvature to focus on objects, near or distant. The pupil, too, is self-adjusting, and these adjustments are automatic, requiring no thought or decision on the part of the individual.

To protect these valuable "cameras," God provided eyelids that open and close 30,000 times a day. These "skin shutters" outside, above, and below the window grow into movable flaps, dry outside like ordinary skin, but moist inside, wiping the window clean every half minute or so by painting fresh salt water over it. There is even a drain for excessive water. As the eye is cleansed by this slow stream of moisture, the excess drains into a bone of the nostril.

The evolutionist says this is the result of a confluence of accidental happenings. What do you think?

Some creatures can move their eyes only from side to side, but the human eye contains six muscles, ingeniously arranged, to lift the eye and roll it from right to left. Another, passing through a pulley, turns it around.

But there is more to the eye than mere mechanics. It has versatility beyond description. It can flash with indignation, be kindled with enthusiasm, expand with devotion, melt with sympathy, stare with fright, leer with villainy, droop with sadness, pale with envy, fire with revenge, twinkle with mirth, and beam with love!

If the lips say one thing and the eyes another, you had better believe the eyes. For confirmation, ask any mother!

It has been said that the eyes of the great Charles Finney constituted the mightiest part of his sermons, and once Martin Luther turned his eyes on a would-be assassin and the villain fled. Under the human eye, even the mighty tiger, with five times the strength of man, slinks back into the jungle.

"He that planted the ear," said the psalmist, "shall he not hear? He that formed the eye, shall he not see?" (Ps 94:9).

You and I stand at the center of a vast circumference of observation. There is no such thing as privacy. We are under the eyes of the cherubim, the seraphim, the archangel, and God! We cannot see the inhabitants of other worlds, but they not only see us, they visit us. In Hebrews 1:14 (Williams) we are told, "Are not the angels all attending spirits sent forth to serve for the sake of those who are going to be unceasing possessors of salvation?" Hagar said, "Thou God seest me" (Gen 16:13). John cried, "His eyes were as a flame of fire" (Rev 1:14). The psalmist said, "His eyelids try, the children of men" (11:4).

Yes, the eyes of God—powerful, pitiful, loving, indignant, merciful—are upon us!

I think you should know that there are eyes more searching, more penetrating, than the eyes of man. They are the eyes of God. He sees our sorrows and assuages them. He sees our perplexities and untangles them. He sees our wants and sympathizes with them.

An asterisk is a star with which a printer focuses attention on a footnote or an explanation. This observer thinks of the myriad stars of heaven as asterisks, calling attention to an *all-seeing God* above us, beneath us, around us, within us! With Him there are no hidden transgressions or forgotten good works.

Our God is not a blind giant stumbling across the heavens or a blind monarch feeling for the steps of his chariot. Have you been wronged? He sees it. Are you plagued with domestic problems? He is aware of it. Are you saying, "My problems are too insignificant for the attention of an omniscient God"? You are wrong. "He that formed the eye, shall he not see?"

Some say God is too far away to see us or to be concerned with our needs, but do you think He sees more poorly than we? We can see the moon, a quarter of a million miles away. We can see our sun, 90 million miles away. We can see many stars, the nearest of which is about 24 trillion miles away, according to the astronomers. If mortal man, with his finite limitations, can see such distances, cannot He who made the eye see our earth—and you?

We know the time will come when human eyes, so exquisitely fashioned and so elegantly strung, hinged, and roofed, will close in death. Loving hands will draw the shades, and God, according to Psalm 127:2, will give His beloved sleep. But is that the end of sight?

Legend has it that the mother of blind Saint Frotebert restored his eyes when she, in sympathy, kissed his sightless orbs. That, of course, is only a legend, but the day is coming when the closed eyes of the righteous will open in response to the kiss of the risen Christ on the resurrection morning! Then vistas supernal will stretch before us as our eyes open on a new and eternal world, and we shall then see with new eyes the things He has prepared for them that love Him.

The following epitaph was found on a gravestone in an old English cemetery:

HERE REPOSES, IN GOD, KATRINA, A SAINT EIGHTY-FIVE YEARS OF AGE AND BLIND. THE LIGHT WAS RESTORED TO HER MAY 10, 1840.

Will it be greater light for you or deeper darkness when you leave this world? The Bible says it will depend on what you did with the available light here. Jesus said, "I am the light of the world. Whoever continues to follow me need never walk in darkness, but he will enjoy the light that means life" (Jn 8:12, Williams).

He also said: "The Spirit of the Lord is upon me, because he hath anointed me to preach the gospel to the poor . . . and recovering of sight to the blind" (Lk 4:18).

Have *your* spiritual eyes been opened? If not, He wants to perform that miracle the moment you are willing to repent, believe, and confess Him (Ro 10:9-10).

5
The Ear

It is both rude and tragic
that its Author should be given
little or no credit for
His engineering skill.

One of the most captivating of all the arts is
architecture, and the study of ancient Egyptian,
Etruscan, Roman, and Renaissance styles of
construction has occupied attention for centuries.

In view of this, it is strange that many who
have traversed the earth to study the art of construction have given less than a passing glance
at one of the greatest architectural wonders of
the world—the human ear.

The ear is more wonderful than any arch ever
lifted, any jeweled pane ever illumined, any Co-
rinthian column ever crowned, or any Gothic
cluster ever elaborated!

In recent years many new and wonderful
things have been discovered about this organ of

hearing, although in a sense the mysterious pathway to the inner ear has been trodden by only two feet—the foot of sound and the foot of God. In point of fact, the finer workings of the inner ear are so complex that few, if any, really understand it.

Although it would be impossible to adequately evaluate this auditory marvel in this brief discourse, I hope to point out some things about it that may give us a clearer insight into the magnitude of its design, and more importantly, the greatness of its Designer. For it is both rude and tragic that engineering skill of such momentousness should be taken for granted, or that its Author should be given little or no credit for His work.

The outer, or visible, area of the ear is in itself a masterpiece of design. It is so constructed as to deflect approaching sounds from a forward position into the ear passage, yet the outer ear is substantially clumsy compared to the *middle* and *inner* ear. As constructive marvels, these defy comprehension and description. Although we are constantly learning more about the mystery and marvel of hearing with the aid of electronics—how, for example, sound waves start the tympanic membrane (eardrum) vibrating—the actual construction remains a phenomenon which man, despite his scientific know-how, cannot approach in design and performance.

For example, the middle ear contains air, while the inner ear is filled with liquid. When sound waves activate the ear drum (an organ capable of handling over 73,000 vibrations per second), the vibrations are transmitted by means of small bones called *ossicles* to the fluid of the inner ear. One of these ossicles is shaped like a tiny stirrup and weighs only 1.2 milligrams. It acts on the fluid like a piston, driving it back and forth in the rhythm of the sound pressure. In turn, the movement of the fluid forces into vibration a thin membrane called the basilar membrane, which transmits the stimulus to a complex structure called the "organ of Corti" containing the ending of the auditory nerves.

Altogether it is a long and complex chain of transmission, too complicated to casually explain or to be readily understood.

One of the many electronic marvels of modern times is the tiny transistor radio, small enough to fit comfortably into the palm of the hand, yet powerful enough to receive transmissions many miles away. No one endowed with ordinary intelligence will deny the existence of a designer back of these miniature marvels, yet many who readily accept a designer behind the transistor deny an intelligent cause behind a transistor composed of muscle and tissue and bone and blood, one of which was perfected millennia before the medium of radio was ever dreamed of—a receiver only 1/4 inch long and 1/250 inch in thickness!

This instrument, standard equipment on man since his creation, is so sensitive it can catch the random rain of air molecules bouncing against it, or withstand the pounding of sound waves strong enough to set the body to vibrating!

Consider, too, its selectivity. In a crowded room it can suppress unwanted noise while concentrating on a selected sound or voice. Of this the finest hearing aid cannot boast!

The ear, so complicated, so multifaceted that numerous anatomical volumes have been dedicated to it, deserves much more than this passing treatment of its functions. But to substantiate that the body and its components are wonders unapproached by the ingenuity of modern science, and to reinforce my next remarks, I quote from an article by George von Bekesy which appeared in the *Scientific American:*

> We have a formidable mechanical problem if we are to extract the utmost energy from the sound waves striking the eardrum. Usually when a sound hits a solid surface, most of its energy is deflected away. The problem the ear has to solve is to absorb this energy. To do so, it has to act as a kind of mechanical transformer, converting the large amplitude of the sound pressure waves in the air to the more forceful vibrations of similar amplitude.

Notice that Dr. von Bekesy says the ear has a problem to solve! Who ever heard of an organ of the body solving a problem? Does an airplane propeller, improperly designed, "solve" its problem? I, for one, would be intensely interested in a mechanism that could do so. Thus far I have heard only of *mechanics* who solve problems, not mechanisms!

Did the ear, by itself, solve the problem of sound absorption, or did the One who made it solve the problem? Incredibly, the evolutionist says the body solved all its problems through millions of years of accidental, coincidental development. But remember, evolution has more than one problem to solve; it has *millions* to solve! And how can a fortuitous chain of events solve anything?

The theorists say evolution has solved this and that problem, but tell me, who is evolution? Did you ever meet him? I will answer that for you in the negative, for evolution is *nothing*. Yet the evolutionist has "nothing" solving all of its problems, even those that bewilder the scientists. And this is the "explanation" of the universe that is being taught our children, from the grades through the university level!

I know some will label me a "square," but I believe there is a mind back of man. If believing that a wonder such as the ear is the work of a God who planned it, built it, understands it, and keeps it functioning, is the mark of a fool, then mark me down as one. I am proud of the appellation!

I believe God created the auditory marvel when He created man and all living things. I see design, and therefore intelligence, in a television set, an electronic computer, a space craft. Why, then, should I be branded an ignoramus because I insist that a phenomenon like the ear was *designed* and *created?*

Let's take a quick look at the importance the Designer and Creator of the ear attaches to it. The Bible has much to say about ears—"itching ears," "obedient ears," "heavy ears," "inclined ears." The Scriptures warn those who deliberately close their ears to truth. "He who has ears to hear, let him hear," said our Lord in Matthew 11:15 (ASB). Some who heard His words were not interested in His message.

Times have not changed.

During His earthly ministry Jesus unstopped many a deaf ear. One day they brought a deaf mute to Him. Putting His fingers in both ears, He cried with a voice that rang clear to the depths of the man's soul, *"Ephphatha!"* meaning "Be opened!" And he who had lived in silence all his life, instantly heard the wash of the waves against the limestone shelving of Galilee.

Jesus Christ is still in the business of restoring deaf ears. He has but to touch the atrophied drum, and sounds never heard before will ring wondrously clear!

The ear's Architect is also described as bending down to hear the supplicant's faintest petition. "I waited patiently for the LORD," said the psalmist, "and he inclined [bent down] unto me and heard my cry" (Ps 40:1). And again in Psalm 116:2: "Because he hath inclined his ear unto me, therefore will I call upon him as long as I live."

You need never fear that He who bequeathed you the gift of hearing will refuse you when you call on Him. His ears are keen, and He has a heart to match!

"He that planteth the ear," said the psalmist, "shall he not hear?" (Ps 94:9).

The answer is *yes!*

6
Growth

I have yet to see a child
become an adult in one
easy (or hard) lesson.

How much thought, if any, have you given to
the mystery of growth?

You may think that's a matter for small, un-
developed minds, but it really isn't. No scientist, however brilliant, can explain growth, how
a seed becomes a flower, how a blob of protoplasm becomes a child, then a man, then a mature mind. The greatest minds stand dumb before the miracle of growth.

The biologists have done their human best to
solve the mystery. They pore over life's building blocks clinically, examining the growth
process under the microscope. They see the
single cell expand, divide, multiply itself, but
still unanswered is the question, "How do
things grow?" Who or what pushes living

things to a certain size, then says "Stop!" What gives the cell the urge and the intelligence to divide and multiply itself? What is the life force that animates all living things? Scientists can make an eye but it cannot see. They can make protoplasm but it cannot live. That's why we must insist that life is planted deeply in the providence of God. Those who are reluctant to credit God with the process call it "nature," but by whatever name it is called, it adds up to miracle.

Jesus reminded His hearers that none could add a single cubit to his height by "taking thought," that is, by conscious effort (Mt 6:27). I remember how exciting growth was to me when I was a boy. There was a certain place by the doorjamb where I measured myself every few days to see how much I had grown. I was not long in learning that there was nothing I could do to force or hasten growth. I couldn't grow taller or faster by wishing. Growth had to come by indirection.

Jesus said, "Consider the lilies of the field, how they grow" (Mt 6:28). This is more than pretty poetry; it points up the dependence of the whole plant world on the invisible forces of creation. You have seen the mystery and miracle of it. Drop a seed into the ground, and it becomes enveloped in a providential process involving the entire universe. Suddenly all the powerful, invisible planetary forces combine and cooperate to produce a flower or tiny blade of grass. Nearly 100 million miles away the sun shines down, the earth turns, the seasons come, the tides move in with the pull of the moon, causing warm air to rise from the oceans in an elaborate air-conditioning system of condensation and evaporation. The lightning flash releases the nourishing nitrogen, drops it to the earth in the rainstorm, and that tiny seed, that green leaf upon which all living things are nourished, is linked up with the total activity of nature. In other words, the smallest blade of grass calls into play the entire planetary system with all its interrelated movements!

Jesus could also have said, "Consider the children, how they grow," for this is no less a mystery. When a boy grows up it's the most imperceptible, quiet thing you've ever witnessed—the growth, I mean, not the boy! He grows without trying; in fact, without knowing. As he grows he is giving his attention to other things—baseball, bike riding, digging underground huts. He doesn't play only because he wants to, but because he has to. Nature keeps him moving with a built-in, self-charging battery of inexhaustible exuberance. He rolls, wrestles, climbs trees, gets awfully dirty and awfully hungry. He eats until you wonder if his legs are hollow! And every few days he hears his mother say, "This kid is growing like a weed. I can't let his clothes out anymore!" But he doesn't know he's growing; at least there has been no conscious effort on his part.

Physical growth is something that always happens indirectly, invisibly, and mysteriously. Doctors can stunt or stimulate growth, but the process is as great a mystery to them today as it ever was.

I must mention also, in passing, the mystery and miracle of the mind's growth. Here is another phenomenon before which science stands dumb, and here again we must wait for time to do its work. Of course we can prod and develop our minds into doing things they would otherwise not do by diligence in study and application, but we can't sit down and say to our minds, "Now you grow, do you hear, and be quick about it." No, little by little—often too little by too little—the mind grows, matures, retains, produces. But you can't shove it beyond certain limits. If you try it you'll find it will balk like a stubborn mule.

Now let's turn to spiritual growth, the thing we're most interested in. We find here some parallels. I know some very sincere people who believe a Christian can reach full spiritual maturity through an experience at an altar, instant maturation, but I have yet to see a child become an adult in one easy (or hard) lesson, either physically or spiritually. We cannot become great Christians by pushing our way into spiritual bigness; in fact, spiritual growth is actually a by-product, a bonus. We automatically "grow up" when we seek and do the will of God and when we serve others. I have seen people become terribly frustrated and distraught because they see so little growth in their spiritual lives. Day after day they get out the yardstick and measure themselves to see if they have grown when growth would be spontaneous if they would just do the things that produce growth. Suppose a boy were to spend every hour of the day and night measuring himself by the doorjamb, crying because he wasn't growing, while all the time neglecting to do the things that produce growth? He won't have to worry about growing if he eats and plays and works and rests normally. He will grow automatically and unconsciously. So with the Christian. He grows as he obeys God's voice, as he does the things Christians are supposed to do.

I am all for the Christian praying and reading his Bible, but I can tell you that you can spend hours on your knees in your bedroom praying, and additional hours with your Bible studying, but if that's all you do, you won't grow an inch. Great Christians are great workers, not just great men of prayer and great Bible students. I wouldn't give a fig for a man's profound understanding of the Bible's mysteries if he only acquires knowledge for the sake of knowledge and for the sake of argument. I want to see him out doing something for others. Long, flowery prayers are meaningless unless they produce power for service. I say again, spiritual growth is a by-product of living out Christ.

I am a man who has known marital happiness for all thirty-five of the years I have been married to the same wife—my first one. Of course we have both worked at making it work, but we haven't sat around trying to figure out how we could be happy and how our love for one another could grow. I may be naive and behind the times, but I think marital happiness and compatibility are natural consequences of love. I don't remember ever working consciously on conjugal felicity. Love just naturally grows until an indissoluble bond is established.

Now apply that principle to loving Jesus Christ. It should require no forcing or cajoling or counseling to keep a Christian happy and satisfied with Him. Great issues are made about whether a Christian should attend the theater or smoke or gamble or drink socially or be sexually abstinent before marriage, et cetera. This is like asking, "Should a man be true to his wife, or a wife to her husband?" Even the secular world believes they should—adultery is grounds for divorce in all fifty states. When I see a married man getting kittenish with a waitress or making like Romeo around a woman other than his wife, I think marital love for that man is dead. Jesus said no man can serve two masters, and by the same token no man can love his wife and seek the arms of another.

I know professing Christians who try to justify clear violations of the Christian position with the shallowest of arguments. They keep asking, "Is it wrong to do this?" and "Is it wrong to do that?" My answer is: If it's questionable, it's probably wrong! I would say a person's relationship with Christ is in trouble when he starts that. A Christian can't consort with the world and love Jesus Christ any more than a husband can be intimate with another woman and love his wife.

Unlike physical growth—a process over which we have little control—spiritual growth is not inexorable. We have little control over bodily growth (up, that is, not out!) but we do control our spiritual growth by habits, thoughts, and conduct. Peter tells us to "grow in grace, and in the knowledge of our Lord and Saviour Jesus Christ" (2 Pe 3:18). You can't separate grace from knowledge. As our knowledge of Him grows, we automatically grow in grace. People whose lives are committed to Jesus Christ will have no problem when it comes to spiritual growth. Last year there were nearly 600,000 divorces in this country. Why? Because a lot of people get married before they know each other. As soon as the glitter of romance wears off, they discover they have little in common and that marriage does not, in itself, solve the problem of physical appetite. So whatever growth there is, it is apart!

As marital happiness is a by-product of a self-giving, shared love, so joy and peace and growth in the Christian life are the result of yielding completely to Christ. I don't understand, for the life of me, why this is considered such a difficult thing to do. It is paradoxical that people work so hard at it. Oh, I know we are all beset by temptations and human weaknesses and discouraging circumstances, but just knowing who Christ is, what He has done for us, is doing for us, should make pleasing Him both easy and delightful. And when we please Him we grow! It is not forced growth, not the result of agonizing importunity, but just the easy, natural, spontaneous outworking of love!

I began this chapter by saying growth is a mystery, and it is. But it's a mystery not infrequently governed by our own desires. As one has so aptly said, "Spiritual development is impeded only by our lack of desire."

7

The Snow

By itself a snowflake is rather insignificant—but consider the might of an avalanche!

As I write these words today it is snowing somewhere. It is always snowing somewhere.

The word *snow* appears twenty-four times in the Bible, sometimes as a noun, sometimes as a verb. It is used as a noun in Job 38:22 where God asks the patriarch, "Hast thou entered into the treasures of the snow?"

Those who have battled with accumulations of "the white stuff" may find it difficult to think of snow as a treasure. Yet, what speaks more eloquently of God's artistry than that which some refer to rudely as the "lowly" snowflake?

Over a century ago the English clergyman and arctic explorer, William Scoresby, classified ninety-six varieties of snowflakes in the arctic circle. They resembled, among other things, stars, coronets, cylinders, globules, hexagons, and pyramids. His research revealed for the first time that no two snowflakes are exactly alike.

Some, in what may only be described as pathetic blindness, see in snow only "the solid form of water which grows while floating, rising or falling in the free air of the atmosphere." But others, who see the hand of God in every aspect of nature, find in snow strong evidences of a Creator capable of not only varying the size, shape, and weight of trillions upon trillions of tiny, crystalline droplets, but of creating billions of human beings, all different and each an object of infinite love and care.

Someone has referred to the Creator as "the God of littles." He may have had reference to the atom, but the universe teems with infinitesimals other than the atom. While our attention is more often directed to the gargantuan—giraffes, elephants, hippopotami, et cetera—there is a whole world of diminutive creatures, most of which are indiscernible to the unaided eye yet perfect in molecular structure.

Snow is one of God's "littles," and it is to these He most often calls our attention. Jesus didn't say, "Consider the universe; the burning suns and the infinitude of the galaxies." He said, "Consider the lilies" (Mt 6:28) and "Behold the fowls of the air" (v. 26). At one point He spoke of the momentousness of a cup of cold water. And He made an imperishable narrative out of a widow's small coin.

In an exclamation of wonderment at the greatness of God, the psalmist reminds us that God knows the number of stars and even calls them by name (Ps 147:4). But Jesus made it a point to remind His hearers that the hairs of their head were numbered! I am interested in a God who can count and name the stars, but I am much more interested in a God who can number the hairs on my head (a task, by the way, that becomes simpler each year!).

Some men, posing as theologians, would have us believe that God is not interested in Johnny's cold or Mary's science test. He may have "started things off," says the self-appointed Bible-shredder, but after that He abandoned man to go it alone.

Anyone who espouses such a dogma must ignore most of what Jesus taught. He said God's main concern is *man*, who is not a mere snowflake in an avalanche, but a special object of the Father's care. He said, "If you then, being evil, know how to give good gifts to your children, how much more shall your Father who is in heaven give what is good to those who ask Him!" (Mt 7:11, NASB). That certainly is not a description of a far-off sovereign, interested primarily in the death of a blazing star or the cycle of a planetary system. It depicts just what Jesus meant it to depict—a loving *Father*, deeply concerned over the smallest detail of our lives. If this is not an accurate picture of God, then Jesus was a fraud, or at best, self-deceived.

It is not necessary to scan the heavens to discover the greatness of God. The Bible doesn't refer to Him as the God of Jupiter, Mercury, or Saturn. Isaiah said, "Behold, God is *my salvation*" (Is 12:2). Paul called Him the God of love and peace (2 Co 3:11); and John refers to Him as the God who will one day wipe away all tears (Rev 21:4).

How mind-staggering it is to know that the God who loves you and me, personally, is also the God of the snowflake!

In a very real sense, however, snow is not a "little" thing. It represents accumulative power. By itself, a snowflake is rather insignificant, but consider the might of an avalanche! A snowflake, although twenty-four times lighter than a raindrop, can represent "a winter wonderland" or a disaster! When those little flakes come too fast and too often, roofs collapse, power poles break, tree limbs snap, mighty locomotives stall, livestock is marooned, and whole towns are buried or cut off from the outside world.

The "lowly" snowflake, in force, can crush the works of men as though they were straws. A single snowflake is nothing, but snow in battalion strength successfully challenges the mind and might of man.

Individually, you and I may be little more than a single flake in a driving snowstorm; but teamed up with others, we can bring righteous pressures to bear that will rout Satan's forces as a village falls before the impact of an avalanche!

This fact spurs me on, challenges and encourages me. If I were all alone in this sin-loving world—a lone voice for God and good—I suspect I would have given up long ago, but I know I am not alone. There are still multiplied thousands who have not bowed to Baal, who are determined that the vocal minority will not have the last word. Just as millions of snowflakes constitute an avalanche, a force before which no man can stand, so I believe God's people, pulling together, can make the name of Christ known and respected across the world.

I am not saying we are a majority; we are anything but that. We are outnumbered, outvoted, and outmaneuvered. But just as one snowflake does not constitute a snowstorm, one dissenter does not constitute a concensus. It is the duty of every Christian to move across the devil's path in a veritable blizzard of prayer, cooperation, and good works.

In the Scriptures, snow symbolizes purity. Ancient peoples believed that snow water had special cleansing powers. It was, in fact, a sort of detergent. Job, touched by this tradition, said, "If I wash myself with snow water, and make my hands never so clean; yet shalt thou plunge me in the ditch, and mine own clothes shall abhor me" (9:30-31). He was speaking to a people influenced by superstition, so he used this symbolism to assure them that water, snow water or otherwise, cannot wash away sin. Only the blood of God's sacrificial Lamb can do that!

Isaiah, too, used snow as a symbol of a cleansed heart. He wrote: "Though your sins be as scarlet, they shall be as white as snow" (1:18). He was referring to the cleansing power of God in response to the humility and repentance of the sinner.

James Nicholson wrote a beautiful hymn, the first two stanzas of which go like this:

Lord Jesus, I long to be perfectly whole;
 I want Thee forever to live in my soul;
Break down every idol, cast out every foe;
 Now wash me, and I shall be whiter than snow.

Lord Jesus, for this I most humbly entreat;
 I wait, blessed Lord, at Thy crucified feet;
By faith, for my cleansing, I see Thy blood flow;
 Now wash me, and I shall be whiter than snow!

Those for whom this prayer is answered are not only fit for heaven; they are also fit for the earth!

The Bible tells us that the occupants of heaven wear white robes. In Revelation, Christ is seen riding on a white horse. John said, "His hairs and his head were white" (Rev 1:14).

Whiteness stands for purity. Even the final judgment of the unrighteous is called the great white throne judgment!

If you would be whiter than snow, turn now to the One who alone can cleanse you of the "like crimson" sin Isaiah describes so graphically.

8

The Heavens

Stars . . . galaxies . . . set in space,
endless space. There are billions upon
billions of everything!

In our childhood we learned this little rhyme:

Twinkle, twinkle, little star;
How I wonder what you are;
Up above the world so high,
Like a diamond in the sky.

Today, thanks to the science of astronomy,
we no longer look at the stars and say, "How I
wonder what they are." Modern telescopes give
us the answer. We know that the stars are suns
like our own, identical except in size.

Yet there is a sense in which the most highly
trained astronomer wonders about the stars, for
science has by no means unraveled all the mysteries
of the universe. In fact, more remain unsolved
than have been answered.

Still, due to modern instruments and computers, new and amazing facts about the heavens are being compiled regularly.

As I have pointed out, stars are suns. Looking up into the star-studded sky on a clear night we have the feeling we are seeing everything that is there, but we are actually seeing only a fraction of the solar system. Many astronomers tell us there are more stars in space than there are grains of sand on all the seashores of earth. The mind can scarcely wrap itself around such vastness.

Let's consider some of the mind-staggering figures released by contemporary astronomers concerning the enormity of space and its "inhabitants."

All are agreed that there are multiplied *billions* of galaxies or "island universes." I am not speaking now of stars, but galaxies, a galaxy being an enormous aggregation of stars. Our own planetary system is part of a galaxy called the Milky Way, and no one has yet boasted of counting all the stars in just this one galaxy! There are multiplied billions!

The number of stars presently visible through modern high-powered telescopes is about sextillion (a one followed by 21 zeros!). Obviously only a fraction of these are visible to the unaided eye. But a 200-inch telescope does a fantastic job of drawing those "invisible" stars into focus. By way of comparison, the naked eye can discern the headlights of an automobile at a distance of about four miles. A 200-inch telescope can detect those same lights, and as separate beams, at about 4,000 miles!

It is therefore obvious that the astronomers have it over us ordinary people, even if we wear trifocals!

Of course we need more than telescopes to measure distance, speed, and energy radiation. This is where physics and chemistry come in. The science of light spectra (called spectroscopy) provides a device which measures temperatures and chemical composition on the surface of the stellar bodies.

Through the science of nuclear physics we are now able to measure, with a reasonable degree of accuracy, the amount of energy discharged by the stars. The average star, according to the experts, radiates energy at the rate of 521 *sextillion* horsepower. (For those of you who consider yourselves mathematicians, that's the number 521 followed by 21 zeros!)

Of what are these stellar bodies composed? Atoms—tiny, microscopic atoms! Yes, atoms compose the stars, the stars compose the galaxies, the galaxies are arranged in clusters, and clusters—well, they are just set in space, endless space. There are billions upon billions of *everything*.

As if this were not enough to challenge the mind, astronomers tell us the entire universe is in a rapid state of expansion! All observable galaxies are *receding* at a rate of thousands of miles a second!

But this is only the *known* world. What about those we cannot see, cannot measure, cannot compute? What lies *beyond* stellar systems picked up by the telescopes? It will probably be necessary to have a conference with God to learn about them!

I don't believe man will ever have his curiosity completely satisfied until, according to 1 Thessalonians 4:17, Christ's people meet Him in the air. I am sure God will reserve some secrets for Himself.

A little more than twenty years ago it was discovered that the method used to measure intergalactic distances (those between the stars in a given galaxy) was inadequate. So astronomers increased their estimates by the factor of ten. We admire them for acknowledging their limitations, yet there is cause to wonder just how much confidence we can place in their figures when, by virtue of only an idea, they expand the universe tenfold!

In the 1940s most astronomers regarded with dubiety the then-popular theory that all the suns and their solar systems were formed simultaneously. Planets were thought to be fragments ejected by their central suns. About that time an eminent astronomer wrote: "The hypothesis of simultaneous creation will not stand up under serious criticism."

But by the late 1940s the idea that "would not stand up under serious criticism" became the prevailing thought!

Surely this should make us cautious about blindly accepting what is so often labeled "established fact" in the realm of science. Many are guesses to be exploded later when more sophisticated equipment is invented and acquired. Too often science discovers that what "couldn't be" is!

Mark Twain, noted more for his wit than piety, tweaked some scientific noses in his book, *Life on the Mississippi*. He wrote:

> In the space of 176 years the lower Mississippi has shortened itself 242 miles. This is an average of a trifle over a mile and a third per year. Therefore any calm person, who is not blind or idiotic, can see that in the Oolitic Silurian Period, just a million years ago next November, the lower Mississippi was upward of one million, three hundred thousand miles long, and stuck out over the Gulf of Mexico like a fishing rod.... There is something fascinating about science. One gets such wholesale returns for such a trifling investment of fact!

Of course Twain was not referring to true science, to which we owe so very much, but in his spoof he underscores some of the incongruous pronouncements which have been released in the name of science.

It is, however, a fact, not a theory, that you and I share a physical oneness with the universe in that the same laws that apply to physics, chemistry, and biology are at work in us. Moses wrote in Genesis 2:7: "And the LORD God formed man of the dust of the ground, and breathed into his nostrils the breath of life; and man became a living soul."

I take this to mean we are made of the same stuff of which God made the universe. What a miraculous feat!

Dr. Frederick H. Giles, Jr., is one of the nation's great astronomers, professor of physics and astronomy at the University of South Carolina. In an article captioned *The Answer to Astronomy's Final Enigma,* he writes:

> As in the case of the universe, the more one learns about God, the more he finds there is to know. More understanding of God is inevitably accompanied by the realization of more widespread and deeper ignorance.
>
> It is humbling to realize that the best astronomers recognize their limited knowledge most keenly, and it is the oldest and wisest saints who most keenly feel their limited knowledge of God. It was the brilliant apostle Paul who reminded his readers that "now we see through a glass darkly."

Those who expect to learn all about God in an

hour's lecture—or during the course of an evening's bull session—will most assuredly be disappointed. Yet we can know Him as a beneficent heavenly Father if we receive His Son, Jesus Christ, as personal Saviour, after which we anticipate the time when we will share the treasures of His infinite knowledge.

9
Trees

A spruce has from 10 to 14 billion cells,
each of which is like a
miniature factory.

Poet Joyce Kilmer (1886-1918) wrote one of
the most widely known poems of the twentieth
century, entitled "Trees." Its composite of sen-
timent and simple philosophy made it an im-
mediate and continuing success. Its most familiar line runs:

> Poems are made by fools like me,
> But only God can make a tree.

Why is there such a marked reluctance on the
part of many to credit God with a direct creative
act? Many men, otherwise intelligent, ascribe
the wonders of creation to some obscure, impersonal benefactor dubbed "Mother Nature." It
is she, it is said, who leafs out the trees in the
spring, who endows all of earth's living or-

ganisms with their incomprehensible instincts, and who keeps the universe on a split-second timetable.

But just who, or what, is Mother Nature? Surely she has not shown up in a test tube, under a microscope, or at the large end of a telescope!

Would it not be just as easy, and far more practical, to speak of nature as "God's handiwork"? Of course this would, in the view of some scientists, be "mixing science with religion." But is it really "scientific" to accept this freak dualism—spirit and matter in two separate compartments, all nicely hermetically sealed?

Is the God of religion not wise or great enough to be the God of science also?

I am not a scientist, but I am deeply interested in science, and my circle of friends includes a number of scientists in various fields. None of these men is hesitant in acknowledging the God in whom, as Paul states in Colossians 2:3, "are hid all the treasures of wisdom and knowledge." Each believes that in Christ resides all the energy and intelligence that keep our hauntingly complex organic universe in shipshape order.

I don't know if the author of "Trees" was conversant with the constitution of the woody plant concerning which he wrote so impressively and poetically, but the chances are he was like most of us. He appreciated their beauty without much knowledge of the growing process that makes a tree one of the most distinctive plants in the botanical spectrum.

Although lacking human intelligence, a tree passes through stages similar to those common to man. It is first an infant, then a juvenile, then an adult. And, barring early disease or injury, it eventually dies of old age.

A tree has transitional cells similar to those in the human body. It is estimated that the spruce, for example, has from 10 to 14 billion cells, each of which is like a miniature factory, performing not only an essential function for the tree, but also manufacturing cellulose and lignin (a relative of cellulose) which make up its cell walls.

It is virtually unbelievable that anyone can be conversant with a tree's ability to subdivide and produce additional living cells and still disavow belief in an intelligent Creator. Try to imagine, if you can, those multiplied billions of tiny cells being assigned a specific task, or more often, a number of tasks. Some, when they subdivide, move to the tree's outer edge and form bark tissue. Others move toward the inside and form the woody tissue. Yet each cell stems from the same initial single cell.

How can a single cell divide into many cells, each performing a different function? You have to be more than a scientist to answer that question. You must be a believer in God!

Science can tell you *what* happens, but not *why*.

What keeps Mother Nature from becoming confused and creating cells for these two tissues, wood and bark, on a one-to-one basis; that is, creating an equal number of cells for each? Should that happen, trees would be half woody tissue and half bark. But of course no one ever saw a tree like that.

Factually, there is no explanation for the predictability of this wondrous cellular ratio in a tree apart from the oversight of God who demands both perfection and constancy.

You have seen trees growing on a hill or mountainside, but have you ever wondered why they grow perpendicular instead of at right angles to the terrain? Let me fill you in on the absorbing story behind this taken-for-granted occurrence.

When a tree grows on a hillside or is abnormally bent from a strong prevailing wind, unnatural cells called "reaction wood" are produced within the tree, forcing the trunk into a vertical alignment and keeping the center of gravity in a relatively stable position.

This specially formed "reaction wood" has a higher than normal lignin content which increases the compressive strength of the lower side of the tree, literally pushing the tree back into a vertical position.

Common sense tells us that randomization doesn't produce order. Who, in proper possession of his faculties, would maintain that "chance" prompts the mother cell of a tree to produce just the right number and kind of daughter cells—or the daughter cell to produce the precise number of cell types needed to produce a balanced organism?

Another phenomenon worthy of mention is the perennial awakening in the spring of plants which have lain dormant and, from all appearances, dead throughout the winter months. Science remains dumb before this mysterious seasonal resurrection. We know only that a perfectly balanced combination of temperature, light, and darkness is required to trigger this incredible restorative process. It is not just a matter of warmth. An unseasonably warm January in a frigid area of our planet would not coax plants out of their dormancy. Periods of light and darkness must be just right and must work in conjunction with warm air.

How simply and beautifully the Bible explains all these wonders. In his letter to the Romans, Paul explains how God reveals Himself to men through creation and their inner consciousness. "For since the creation of the world," he writes, "His [God's] invisible attributes, His eternal power and divine nature, have been clearly seen, being understood through what has been made" (Ro 1:20, NASB).

He then adds, "So that they [men] are without excuse."

It is not easy to sympathize with those who say they have searched for God in vain. This is tantamount to saying God is elusive, and this I cannot buy. God is so evident that only the willfully blind miss Him! He has not only written His name across the sky; He has written it in nature and on every heart! Man without God is man without an excuse!

Speaking not as a scientist, but as one with, I trust, a measure of mature judgment and an honest heart, I must say I encounter no difficulty in accepting a Creator who made the worlds and who keeps them in proper working order. I believe also in a God who made the trees and who made me; who would have made a perfect "me" except for my will, which, unlike a tree, rebels against His will. Trees do not inherit an imperfect moral nature, but men do. That is why God chose to provide a perfect Saviour for men, One who took upon Himself their deserved punishment on Calvary's cross—a tree!

How do you and I benefit from that sacrifice? By appropriating for ourselves His complete sacrifice through the medium of repentance and faith.

Remember that the God who made the tree made you! But, unlike a tree, you have an immortal soul, one into which He breathed the breath of eternal existence—somewhere. Thus, long after all trees are gone and forgotten, the soul will live on.

But where? This is a decision only you can make. The Bible says, "But as many as received him [Christ], to them gave he power [the right] to become the sons of God, even to them that believe on his name" (Jn 1:12).

This, like the making of a tree, is something only God can do.

10
Water

God knew man's needs in advance.

Technically, water is an incredible mixture of hydrogen and oxygen, combined in just the right proportion to serve man's needs. It is, indisputably, one of God's crowning miracles.

Frozen, it makes life easier and safer. In the form of snow it provides the earth with a blanket, storing millions of gallons of water on plains and mountaintops for later use. In the form of rain, it feeds vegetation and rivers, fills lakes and oceans. In the form of clouds it protects living things from the scorching summer heat. As steam, it presses clothes, drives machinery, generates electricity, and performs an impressive variety of services for mankind.

Water is also an ingenious air conditioner. It has a prodigious capacity for storing heat energy, a fact that makes life possible for man. Without water we could not survive our winters, for the heat stored in the oceans provides climatic moderation in the winter. Their waters retain the sun's heat, then release it during the frigid months so the cold will not surpass levels of human tolerance. What is more, the oceans are so distributed as to best accomplish this thermal effect.

Scientists say water is the closest approach to a true universal solvent, dissolving most materials with ease; yet how fortunate for us that it doesn't dissolve sand or rocks! The world's shorelines, as we know, are protected by these insoluble substances. If coastal areas consisted of ordinary soil, they would quickly erode, causing the inundation of much of the earth's surface.

Sea water is 800 times heavier than air, yet when it is vaporized by the sun's rays it becomes lighter than air and is drawn up into the atmosphere. Providentially, it leaves the salt behind. Were it otherwise, rain would have a saline content and would kill plants, and poison man's water supply.

According to Genesis 1:6-7, the oceans and clouds were not separated before the creation of man. Great blankets of vapor must have hugged the earth, resulting in a thick, global fog. God knew man could not long survive such an environment, so He girdled the earth with an atmospheric wrapping which separated the clouds from the oceans. This is what He did:

God said: Let there be a firmament between the waters to divide waters from waters; so God made the firmament and separated the waters under the firmament from the waters above the firmament; and it was so (Gen 1:6-7, Berkeley).

Another phenomenon is the earth's rain cycle. As the sun shines on the ocean's surface, it draws into the upper atmosphere about 5,435 tons of water per square mile of ocean surface. This vapor rises to considerable heights, then moves, by means of air currents, across the continents. When this warm, vapor-saturated air cools, it condenses into innumerable tiny droplets so small that about 8 million are needed to make a single drop of rain! As this condensation occurs, clouds are formed; and as the air cools, the tiny droplets fuse into larger drops until the air is unable to support them. The larger drops reach the earth in the form of rain.

What kind of a conference did these elements hold in order to work out this ingenious plan—water cooperating with the sun, wind cooperating with the atmosphere, and the earth's rotational rate cooperating with them all? Who, in fact, decided rain was necessary to make things grow, to clean the air of impurities, and to sustain life?

If we listen to a growing number of scientists and educators, we will conclude that it was all a giant mathematical accident.

How does this immense amount of water,

drawn into the atmosphere, return to its source? If it didn't, you know, the world's great bodies of water would eventually be depleted.

Well, God settled that problem by draining all continents and major islands by means of giant rivers. In Africa there is the Nile, in the Congo the Niger, in North America we have the St. Lawrence, the Columbia, the Colorado, and the Mississippi. In South America there are the Amazon and the Orinoco; in Europe, the Rhine, the Rhone, the Danube, and the Volga; in Asia there are the Yellow River, the Ganges, the ancient Tigris, and Euphrates.

Of course there are many, many others, but these are the major, better-known rivers.

But aren't these rivers just the natural result of draining water seeking its own level? If this were so, why are there not multiplied thousands of major rivers instead of only a few? An honest appraisal demands that the present arrangement be the result of an intelligently worked-out plan. If civil engineers were given the task of draining a continent and had the means to do it, they would use several large drains, not innumerable little ones.

That's how God did it!

Think of the vital part mountain ranges play in the distribution of water. Without them we would have no rivers, for the shaded (chilled) sides of the mountains create vast condensing surfaces where clouds yield their moisture in the form of rain and snow. That condensation is then fed into streams and rivers, assuring a continual supply of fresh water for man and growing things.

The prophet Isaiah was intrigued by this arrangement. He wrote:

> Who has measured the water in the hollow of His hand, marked off the heavens with a span, enclosed the dust of the earth in a measuring basket, weighed the mountains in scales or the hills in a balance? (Is 40:12, Berkeley).

Isaiah knew Someone had to plan all these intricate combinations and percentages. If God did not measure the waters in the hollow of His hand, there would be no dry land. If man had been given the task of creating the earth, would he have created more water than dry land? Certainly not. He might have stuck a few pretty little lakes and streams here and there, but he would most certainly not have made only 29 percent of the earth dry land. Yet scientists now tell us this is exactly the right percentage; if it were even equally divided between land and water, all life would perish.

Seventy-one percent water is exactly the right percentage!

The water which covers nearly three-fourths of the earth's surface has an average depth of two miles. The world's oceans contain some 300 million cubic miles of water, forming an immense life-giving and life-sustaining reservoir.

How did it all happen? Where did it all come from? As far as we know, ours is the only planet in our solar system with water. Most of the matter in the universe consists of flaming gases (as in the stars), or frozen solids drifting through space.

Some years ago *Life* magazine carried an article in which the author stated: "Only with a hairline band of the immense temperature spectrum of the universe—ranging through millions of degrees—can water manifest itself as a liquid."

Why did it manifest itself as a liquid on this planet? Because God knew man's needs in advance!

The late Fred Meldau, in his book, *Why We Believe in Creation, Not Evolution*, summed it up tidily:

> It is as easy to believe that the Mona Lisa came into existence by stray bits of variously colored pigments being hurled through space that happened to hit a canvas now in the Louvre as to believe that this marvelous world came about by chance.

Why did God create the earth with all of its wonderful appointments? The Bible says He created it as a habitat for man—man whom He created and loved. But along with all these benefactions man was given the option of hating Him or loving Him back. Most have chosen to hate Him, proving a measure of divine love and patience inconceivable to the human mind.

Water is but one of God's many gifts to man, but are you thankful for it? Have you ever expressed your thanks in prayer? Have you ever singled it out as one of God's greatest love gifts to you?

I trust you will never see it rain, or drink a glass of water, or gaze upon a body of water, without at least bowing your heart in reverential thanksgiving for this gift of divine love.

11

The Earth

If its size varied as much as
10 percent either way, all life
would cease to exist.

Abraham Lincoln once said, "I can see how it might be possible for a man to look down on the earth and be an atheist, but I cannot see how he could look up into the heavens and say there is no God."

I concur with Mr. Lincoln except for one point; I don't understand how a person can be an atheist no matter where he looks! Whether one gazes at the heavens or looks under his feet, there is abundant evidence of intelligent design and planning.

Many who stoutly deny they have ever seen a miracle see many every day. I realize they don't consider them miracles, but in the context of the dictionary definition—"Any wonderful or amazing thing, fact or event"—who can deny that we are enveloped with miracles? Moreover, each evidences the skill of an omnipotent hand. To call them "accidents" is to close one's eyes to every normal and practical conclusion.

Today everyone knows what a thermostat is. I doubt whether our younger friends will ever fully appreciate this electronic custodian, but many of us remember (and not with nostalgia!) the old coal stoves and furnaces that had to be stoked with shovels and that were provokingly temperamental. These, fortunately, are for the most part relics of the past. Modern homes come equipped with indicators on the wall that may be set to a desired temperature and forgotten.

How was this revolutionary improvement in temperature control brought into existence? Through evolution? Natural selection? Survival of the fittest? Foolish questions, you say? Of course. And remember just how foolish they are the next time someone tells you the earth's friendly environment just "happened."

Let's talk about the earth's incredible system of climate control, and after doing so, I want you to ask yourself if there is a greater chance that it "evolved" than that the thermostat in your house is the product of a fortuitous combination of elements.

Science tells us the size of the earth is just right to sustain life; if it were a little smaller or larger, human beings could not exist upon it.

The diameter of the earth, according to the *Encyclopaedia Britannica,* is approximately 8,000 miles. This means that if you were able to bore a hole in it 8,000 miles deep, the auger would emerge from the other side. But why 8,000 miles? Why not, say, 9,500 miles? Because adding even 1,000 miles to the diameter of the earth would be disastrous. The weight of the air would double, as would the amount of oxygen. This would result in such an increase in the amount of water that the earth would be inundated!

Suppose, on the other hand, the earth were lighter than it is. This would so decrease its gravitational pull that it would retain less air than is necessary. The lighter gases would escape, leaving only the heavier ones, such as carbon dioxide. This, in turn, would affect the volume of the atmosphere's density, making organic life impossible. Atmospheric conditions here would approximate those on the moon.

"The earth is unique," writes Patrick Moore in his book, *A Guide to the Planets,* "because it is the only world in the solar system upon which we could survive." This will be confirmed, I am confident, when our space scientists have completed their examination of all the other planets in our system.

But suppose the earth were smaller in diameter than it is, say, 7,200 miles instead of 8,000. This is what would happen. Due to the lessening of the atmospheric mantle, our globe would be reduced to an ice-clad waste. In fact, if the earth's size varied either way as much as 10 percent, all life would cease to exist.

Yet your child is probably being taught in his science class that all this just "happened," that it was a trillion-to-one set of odds in a vast universe! And parents are sitting still for this!

Any child out of the infant stage knows that if he gets too close to a fire he will be burned, and if, on a very cold night, he gets too far away from it he will freeze. But what draws us to a fire when we are cold, and determines how close we can get to it without being burned? Not instinct or impulse or compulsion, but *intelligence*. Without intelligence we would leap into the fire, or withdraw from it and freeze to death.

How can we account for the earth being exactly the right distance from the sun in relation to the amount of light and heat it radiates? It is 93 million miles away from us—exactly the right distance. If it were closer, all organic life would perish. If it were farther away, the earth would be a block of ice.

The sun is just the right distance away to lift water from our rivers, lakes, and oceans in the form of vapor, thus ensuring essential rainfall. Without the sun's heat in its present portion, winds to propel and diversify the clouds would not be produced. Even slight changes in the earth-sun relationship, in terms of distance, would make of this planet an arctic waste or a burning desert.

How can we explain, minus God, how the sun's light, traveling at a speed of 186,000 miles a second, reaches the earth in a perfect state, creating just the right amount of heat, light, energy, electromagnetic radiation, gamma rays, X rays, ultraviolet rays, infrared rays, and radio waves?

And what about the earth's size and mass? If the earth were 10 percent larger in diameter, the weight of the air would double. This would double the amount of oxygen, and the sum total of water would be greatly increased, possibly resulting in the earth's complete inundation!

If the oceans were deeper, say the oceanographers, an excessive amount of carbon dioxide and oxygen would be absorbed, making vegetable life on the earth's land surfaces impossible. Would you say this is a coincidence?

If the atmosphere around the earth were thinner, the millions of meteors that now become harmless cinders as they enter it would strike the earth, leaving it pockmarked and uninhabitable. Most scientists believe the moon's craters were caused by errant meteorites that were not impeded because of that planet's thin atmosphere. But God didn't make the moon for man; He made the earth for him. That's why we have this protective provision.

The moon, too, is just the right distance from the earth. Were it only half as far away or twice its present diameter, it would affect the ocean tides so adversely that low-lying islands and coastal plains would be inundated, and tides would go hundreds of miles up some rivers that empty into the sea. If, on the other hand, the moon were smaller and farther away its effect on the tides would be negligible and we would be starved for the oxygen we derive from the oceans.

For the earth to be habitable, it must have an adequate supply of light and heat, a uniform distribution of water, and an atmosphere of proper density and composition. *Our planet has all three.* The atmosphere is made up of 78 percent nitrogen, 21 percent oxygen, with smaller percentages of argon, carbon dioxide, water vapor (humidity), neon, helium, methane, krypton, xenon, hydrogen, ozone, and several other gases. All of these, however, exist in much larger quantities in other areas of the universe. Why are they so uniformly distributed on earth, making life possible?

The intelligent answer is *God.*

Suppose our atmosphere contained, say, 50 percent oxygen instead of 21. Every combustible substance on earth would become highly inflammable. If a bolt of lightning struck a tree, the whole forest would ignite; in fact, it would explode like a bomb.

But what if the oxygen content of the air were only, say, 10 percent? Fire would then not burn. Imagine life on earth without fire!

Every schoolchild knows that oxygen, drawn into the lungs, is taken up by blood cells and distributed to all parts of the body, that it is essential to the function of the mind, that it burns the food in each body cell, that it produces carbon dioxide and water vapor which the lungs expel into the air.

What happens, by the way, when we exhale and expel it into the air? Plants absorb the carbon monoxide, separate it into carbon and oxygen, combine it with the hydrogen of the water in their roots, which in turn produces leaves, fruit, flowers, and all forms of plant life. While this is going on, plants are releasing oxygen for men, animals, and plants to breathe!

Who instructs the plant to retain the carbon and release the oxygen? Whoever it is, we can be eternally grateful to Him. If the plants ever got mixed up, mankind would be done for in less than five minutes!

Without the carbon dioxide we give the plants, they would die. Without the oxygen they give us, we would die.

How incredible that many people have convinced themselves this is all *chance*—an accident!

When the psalmist said, "The earth is the LORD'S, and the fulness thereof; the world, and they that dwell therein" (Ps 24:1), he proved himself a much smarter man than some who live 3,500 years later!

12

What Is Your Life?

The whole world wants to know!

"What do you want most to know?" The question was asked a few years ago of a representative number of teenagers.

The majority answered, "We want to know why we are here. We want to know what life is all about. We want to know where we came from and where we are going!"

Teenagers are not the only ones who are seeking answers to these questions. The whole world wants to know.

To many the question is not so much "Why am I here?" but "How do I get out of this mess?" The title of a well-known Broadway play comes to mind: *Stop the World. I Want to Get Off.* Multitudes are afraid to go on living but more afraid to take their own lives. To their tortured minds, birth is an injustice.

How can these fearful and disillusioned ones

be helped? Only as they are convinced that everyone's life has a purpose and a plan. This requires belief in a higher power, a God who cared enough for His creatures to break into human history in the person of His Son, and who provided a means whereby sinners could relate, on a father-child basis, to a holy God.

Short of this there is indeed no rhyme or reason to life.

I have often said that if I were to throw away my Bible, I would want to throw away my life. Purpose is lost when men lose the Bible, for the world has no fitting substitute guide.

One of the most widely honored and often quoted men at the turn of the century was Samuel Langhorne Clemens, better known by his pen name, Mark Twain. The literary world still bows before his wit and skill with words, yet Twain's life was characterized by forlornness and pessimism. Although most of his writings were humorous, his biographers all agree he was not a happy man. Loaded with talent, he never did come up with the right answers.

In his autobiography he wrote:

> A myriad of men are born; they labor and struggle and sweat for bread; they squabble and scold and fight; they scramble for little mean advantages over each other. Age creeps upon them and infirmities follow; shame and humiliation bring down their pride and vanities.

Those they love are taken from them, and the joy of life is turned to aching grief. The burden of pain, care, misery, grows heavier year by year. At length ambition is dead; longing for relief is in its place.

It comes at last—the only unpoisoned gift earth has for them—and they vanish from a world where they were of no consequence, where they achieved nothing, where they were a mistake and a failure and a foolishness; where they left no sign that they had ever existed—a world that will lament them a day and forget them forever.

Twain struck a similar note in his book *The Mysterious Stranger*, published in 1916, six years after his death. It contains this line: "Life is all a dream—a grotesque and foolish dream."

This was Mark Twain, of the nimble mind and quick wit; a man with a rare literary gift—but, alas, a man without God! It is easy to pity him, this talented person who, pathetically, missed life's best because, in the great struggle, he failed to recognize himself as a part of a great and lofty purpose.

Had Twain been religiously inclined, he might have found Buddhism to his liking, for Buddha refers to what he calls "The Four Sorrows" in his teachings. The first is sickness, the second death, the third old age, and the fourth "to be born into the world." This was essentially Twain's philosophy—despair. It is also the philosophy of most people who overlook or

91

reject God's wonderful plan for man as outlined in the Bible.

To come in contact with those who sincerely and selflessly embrace the Christian faith is to have an awareness of the clear contrast between the non-Christian's philosophy of futility, and the buoyant hope of those who know and love God.

The believer *knows* where he came from, why he is here, and where he is going!

Of course if the Bible is not God's inspired Word, Mark Twain and Buddha may have been right—life *is* a meaningless episode between the cradle and the grave. The apostle Paul understood this, and he wrote, "If we have hope in Christ for this life only then of all people we are most to be pitied" (1 Co 15:19, Berkeley). He also had something to say about the dreary viewpoint of men like Twain and others who espouse the doctrine of futility. In 1 Corinthians 1:21 he states that the world cannot know God through wisdom alone. Surely this has been proved often enough. Although civilization owes much to the world's great minds, most, in their search for knowledge, have missed God. This squares with what the Bible declares, namely, that God cannot be properly comprehended by rationalism. He cannot be "demonstrated" scientifically or visually. Those who insist on seeing Him with their own eyes, hearing Him with their own ears, and touching

Him with their own hands, will never be convinced.

"Why is it you religious people can't prove anything?" a student asked Dr. J. Edwin Orr at the conclusion of a lecture on campus. "A biologist can take you to his microscope, and an astronomer to his telescope, but you religious people are always speaking about taking things by faith."

Yes, and for good reason: "The just shall live by faith" (Ro 1:17). In the Christian realm, believing is seeing. The believer has all the evidence he needs *within*. And although salvation is not something one studies under a microscope or tests with litmus paper, yet it is convincing enough to cause millions to forsake all to follow Jesus Christ. Intangible, it is as convincing as if it could be touched, heard, seen, and tasted! It is seeing with the eye of faith. It is hearing God speak to the human heart. It is "the evidence of things not seen."

There is no way to *explain* a Christian except on a supernatural basis, and by the term Christian I don't mean a Gentile or an American citizen. The Bible defines a Christian very narrowly. There is a marked difference between a real Christian and a person who is merely religious. Contrary to popular opinion, a Christian is not one who has merely attached himself to the teachings of Jesus as his ethical standard, or the Ten Commandments and the Sermon on the

Mount as his life patterns. A Christian is not someone with something on his mind; he is a person with Someone in his *heart!* And more than the right hand of fellowship, or a few drops of water sprinkled on the head, is required to put a person on the road to heaven.

A Christian is one who enjoys an intimate Father-child relationship with God through faith in the person and work of His Son, Jesus Christ. The apostle John wrote: "But as many as received Him [Jesus], to them He gave the right to become children of God, even to those who believe in His name" (Jn 1:12, NASB). This, you can readily see, is much more than just believing in God or the Bible. It is more than accepting a church creed, saying prayers, or receiving a reward for faithful attendance. It is more than reciting the Apostles' Creed. It is receiving, by faith, the Lord Jesus Christ as your personal Saviour and the Lord of your life.

Only an act of repentance and faith can make you a child of God. Modern theology says God is the Father of all, but this is true only in the sense that God created all men. A *saving* relationship is dependent upon faith in Christ. To the Messiah-rejecting Pharisees, Jesus said, "You are of your father the devil" (Jn 8:44, NASB). He made it crystal clear that those who rejected Him had rejected the Father. "Every man who believes in me is believing in the one who sent me: and every man who sees me is eeing the one who sent me. I have come into he world as light, so that no one who believes n me need remain in the dark" (Jn 12:44-46, Phillips).

Here we have the explanation for the spiritually darkened minds of men like Mark Twain who, despite many talents, live and die in uncertainty and despair.

How devoid of sense and direction is life if we abandon the hope of the Gospel! Viewed from strictly the human standpoint, it bears out the doctrine of Buddha that there are four great sorrows, one of which is to be born. Viewed from the human standpoint alone, there must be agreement with Mark Twain who wrote, "The world laments us a day and forgets us forever."

But this is not the Christian's appraisal of life, or death. The believer does not accept the "unfortunate happenstance" as an interpretation of life. Rather, he is convinced that he is the product of a loving heavenly Father's divine ingenuity, that he has a glorious destiny if he is obedient.

In my library is a book bearing the title, *Twice Born Men*. It bears the personal testimonies of twenty-six businessmen who found purpose and direction in their adult years through faith in Jesus Christ. They represent a sweeping range of professions—banking, law, engineering, science, art, medicine, sports. One was even a professional criminal, another a former

95

member of the Nazi party, and a number were former alcoholics. All had something in common; they were aimless and helpless—until they met Christ!

As one reads these thrilling Christian testimonies he cannot avoid seeing the sharp contrast between what these professional men discovered in Christ and the bleak philosophies of others, brilliant in their own right, who never came to grips with *reality* as it centers in Jesus Christ.

My friend, *you* too may find the place in life that spells purpose and peace, but first you must be willing to look for it in Christ. There is no other approach to God. "No man cometh unto the Father, but by me" (Jesus, in Jn 14:6).

Invite Him into your life now and discover the true purpose of life—and the victory which is experienced even in death!

Moody Press, a ministry of the Moody Bible Institute, is designed for education, evangelization and edification. If we may assist you in knowing more about Christ and the Christian life, please write us without obligation to: Moody Press, c/o MLM, Chicago, Illinois 60610.